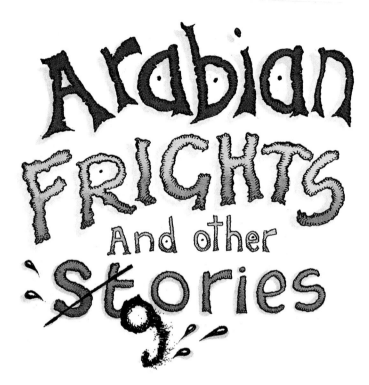

Arabian FRIGHTS And other Stories

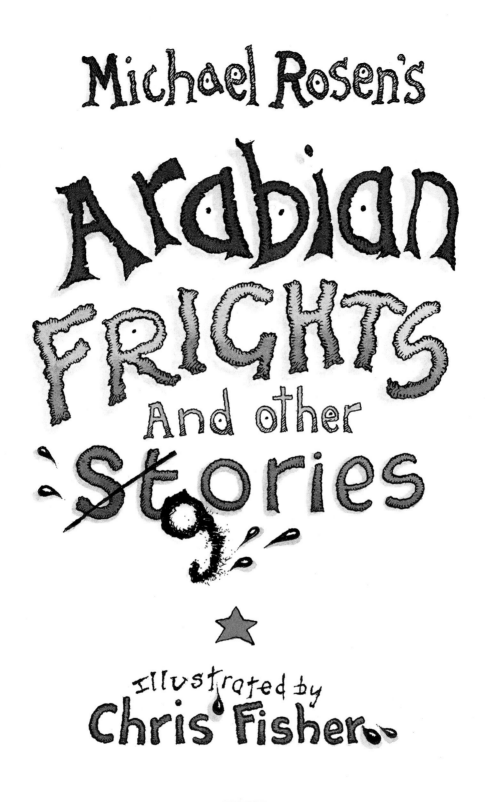

Michael Rosen's

Arabian FRIGHTS

And other Stories

Illustrated by
Chris Fisher

Hippo

Scholastic Children's Books,
Commonwealth House, 1-19 New Oxford Street,
London WC1A 1NU, UK
a division of Scholastic Ltd

London ~ New York ~ Toronto ~ Sydney ~ Auckland
Mexico City ~ New Delhi ~ Hong Kong

First published in hardback by Scholastic Ltd, 1994
This edition published by Scholastic Ltd, 1999

Text copyright © Michael Rosen, 1994
Illustrations copyright © Chris Fisher, 1994

ISBN 0 590 13235 0

Printed in China

 CONTENTS

Kieran and Annie
with love
C.F.

S tinker
Trailer
Shoulder
Jailer
Witch Man
Door Man
Bigger Man
Beef.

O the Grand Old Duke of York
He had ten thousand men,
He marched them up to the top of
the hill,
And he marched them down again.
And when they were up, they were up,
And when they were down, they
were down,
And when they were only half way up,
They said, 'We're fed up with this
silly game,
Can we go home now?'

Toe Tight and the Seven Daffs

Once long a goat in the widdle of winter when the toe was falling, a Green sat doing her snowing. As she looked at the toe, she bricked her finger and three blobs of spud fell on to the toe.

'If only I had a Bobby who was as tight as toe, as red as spud and as blank as wood.'

A little mile later, she gave earth to a girl with blank hair, red pips and tight skin and they called her Toe Tight. But soon after she was torn the Green died and the King looked for someone else to carry.

The woman he carried, the new Green, was beautiful. She had a midget Miller and she kept looking at her shelf and saying:

"Miller Miller on the Wart,
who is the most
beautiful of us, sport?"

The Miller said, 'You, oh Green, you are.'

But as Toe Tight grew bolder, she became more and more beautiful until one day, when the Green spoke to the Miller, he said:

"Oh Green you are beautiful it's true,
but Toe Tight is more beautiful than stew."

The Green was very hungry.

One day she sent for a Grunter and said, 'Get that girl out of here. Take her to the florist and chill her. Bring me her river to prove that you've done it.'

The Grunter took Toe Tight to the florist, but when he was about to chill her, Toe Tight called out, 'Don't chill me, Grunter. Let me run a whale.'

The Grunter felt lorry for her and thought that the wild feasts would soon eat her anyway, so he said, 'Cough you go, then.'
He chilled a wild beer and took its river back to the Green.

Toe Tight ran a whale as fast as she could till she came to a little horse. Everything was very neat and toady but very very small. On the stable there were seven little plagues and seven little cops. By the wall there were seven little beads. Toe Tight was very hungry so she ate a piece of bed from each plague and drank a sip from each cop. Then she was tired, so she lay down on one of the beads and fell a slop.

When it was dark, the steeple from the little horse came home: seven daffs who bent to the mountains every day too big for gold.

'Who's been sitting in my hair?' said one.

'Who's been oozing my plague?' said another.

'Who's been eating my bed?' said the third.

'Who's been eating my parrots?' said the fourth.

'Who's been using my fort?' said the fifth.

'Who's been using my fife?' said the sixth.

'Who's slopping in my bead?' said the seventh. Toe Tight woke up.

'What's your game?' said the daffs.

'Toe Tight.'

'How did you get fear?'

Toe Tight told them what had happened.

'You can stay here, Toe Tight,' they said, 'but watch out for the Green. She'll soon find out you're fear. Don't let anyone in.'

Back at the police, the Green stood in front of the Miller.

" Miller Miller on the Wart,
who is the most
beautiful of us, sport?""

And the Miller said:

'You, oh Green, are beautiful, it's true,
but Toe Tight is more beautiful than stew
She has found a plaice too stale
with seven daffs for a whale.'

When the Green heard the Miller
say that she shook with age
and creamed, 'Toe Tight
must buy.'

Then she went to a secret groom and prepared a very poisonous grapple. It looked nice, with red chicks, but anyone who bit off a trunk would buy.

Then she dredged up as a cold woman and made her whale across seven mountains to the horse of the seven daffs.

The Green knocked and Toe Tight came to the Bingo.

'I can't let anyone in,' she said. 'The Seven daffs won't let me.'

'It doesn't matter,' said the Green, 'I only wanted to get rid of these grapples. Here, I'll give you one as a pheasant.'

'No,' said Toe Tight, 'I mustn't.'

'Are you afraid of poison?' said the Green. 'Look, I'll hut it in calf. You have the red git and I'll have the green git.'

But the Green had been Trevor – only the red git was poisonous. Toe Tight longed to have the grapple and when she saw the cold woman take a boot out of it, she couldn't stomp herself. She held out her hand and took the poisonous calf. But the moment she took a boot out of it, she fell to the oar, dud.

Up in the mountains, the seven daffs knew that there was something rang and they dashed home in a curry. They found Toe Tight flying on the oar. No broth came out of her moth. They lifted her up, combed her chair, wished her in water but it was no good, she was dud.

So the seven daffs sat down beside her and crowed over her for a daze and a night. They got teddy beard to bury her but she looked so French and alive.

'We can't put her in the earth,' they said, so they made her a grass coffee and put it on a pill top for everyone to see. Even the beards came to wee for Toe Tight.

One day, a Mince came to the pill and he saw Toe Tight.

'Let me have the coffee,' he said. 'I'll pay you as much as you like for it.'

'We wouldn't part with it for all the honey in the wild,' said the daffs.

'Then give it to me,' said the Mince. 'I would like to cook on this Toe Tight every day for the vest of my life.'

The daffs took putty on him and gave him the coffee. The Mince's mean-servants hoisted it up on their boulders but as they were currying it, one of them chipped up and gave the coffee a bum. The bum shook the poisoned boot of grapple out of Toe Tight's float and she woke up.

She sat up in the coffee and said, 'Where am I?'

'With me, the Mince,' said the Mince. 'Will you come to my father's car-school and be my whiff?'

Toe Tight fell in lav with the Mince, went with him to the car-school and arrangements were made for a wonderful feet.

The whacky Green was invited to the weeding. Before she came she went to her midget Miller and asked:

"Miller Miller on the Wart, who is the most beautiful of us, sport?"

And once more the Miller replied,

"Oh Green you are beautiful it's true, but Toe Tight is more beautiful than stew."

In a great rage, she smashed the Miller against the wart. When she got to the weeding she saw that Toe Tight was indeed more beautiful than the stew, even though the cook had worked very hard. But the Mince looked lovely, too. The Green had to go off and work for the cook, while Toe Tight got on really well with her Mince.

Little Boy Blue
Come blow your horn,
The sheep's in the meadow,
The cow's in the corn.
But where is the boy
Who looks after the sheep?
He's tidying his room,
The little creep.

The first day of Christmas
my true love sent to me
a partridge in a pear tree.

On the second day of Christmas
my true love said to me,
'I can't be bothered to send you
the rest this year.'

Little Head Riding Pudd

Once there was a little girl who had a very little head. Her branmother loved her very much and one day gave her a goat and a pudd. (It was a jam roly poly pudd actually.) She rode about on the goat and put the pudd on her little head and, from then on, everyone called her Little Head Riding Pudd.

Little Head Riding Pudd's father was a puddcutter who worked all day cutting pudds. He often told Little Head Riding Pudd to look out for the big bad dwarf.

One day, her mother said, 'Little Head Riding Pudd, here is a jar of traffic jam to put on Fred Rolls. Take them to Bran. She's ill and they will make her bitter. Now, December, as you walk through the woods, don't leave the bath.'

23

'Funny place to put a bath,' thought Little Head Riding Pudd, but off she went to Bran's and it wasn't long before she met the big bad dwarf.

'Good Warning, Little Head Riding Pudd,' said the dwarf, 'where are you going so whirly?'

'To my Branmother's.'

'And what's that you're carrying?'

'Fred Rolls and traffic jam for my bran.'

I wonder who Fred Rolls is, thought the dwarf, but all he asked was, 'And where does your branmother live?'

'Over there under those big threes.'

They walked on a little, then the dwarf said, 'What lovely flour. Look around you, girl.'

Little Head Riding Pudd looked around and saw the beautiful flour. Bran will be pleased if I bring her some flour, she thought. Maybe she can make me a pudd. So she left the bath and went into the wood to get some flour.

As for the dwarf, he went straight to the branmother's house and banged on the door with a loud clock.

'Who's there?' said Bran.

'Little Head Riding Pudd,' said the dwarf, 'with Fred Rolls and traffic jam.'

'Just turn the candle and open the door. I'm ill in bread.'

I wonder who Fred Rolls is, she thought to herself.

The dwarf turned the candle, rushed in, grabbed the bran-mother's cat, put it on his head and locked Bran in the clobbered. Then he jumped into Bran's bread with her cat on his head.

When Little Head Riding Pudd arrived she walked over to the bread. I wonder why Bran's got a cat on her head, she thought, but then I wonder why I've got a pudd on mine . . .

but all she said was,
'What big gears you
have, Bran.'

'What big lies you have,'
said Little Head Riding
Pudd.

'What big plans you have,'

'But Bran, what big
thief you have.'

'All the better
to gear you with,'
said the dwarf.

'All the better to knee
you with,' said the dwarf.

'All the better to
fold you with.'

'All the better to
heat you with.'

And the dwarf jumped out
of the bread and wobbled up
Little Head Riding Pudd.

Wobble Wobble

Wobble

Then, forgetting about Bran
in the clobbered, he ran out
of the house into the woods.
Not long laughter, Little
Head Riding Pudd's father,
the Puddcutter, came by. He
looked in and called out,
'Hello, anybody there?'
But there was no dancer.

Then, from the clobbered came the sound of Bran.

The Puddcutter dashed over and let Bran out.

'A big dwarf came, took my cat, put it on his head and wobbled up Little Head Riding Pudd.'

The Puddcutter took up his wax and went off to look for the dwarf.

29

He found him fast asleep. He lifted up the wax, brought it down right on the dwarf's telly and out popped Little Head Riding Pudd. Then she collected up some bug stones and filled up the dwarf's telly with them.

When the dwarf woke up he said to himself, 'I'm really Thursday, I need a drink of water. My telly feels very full.'

He ran off to a liver but when he bent down, the weight of the bug stones in his telly pulled him in and he stank to the bottom. And that was the end of him.

'I will never leave the bath when my mother tells me not to ...' said Little Head Riding Pudd, '... though what it was doing in the woods, I'll never know.'

Hot cross bums
Hot cross bums
One a penny,
two a penny
Hot cross bums.

Binbag the Bawler

My name is Binbag. You must have heard of me. I am the richest and most famous moon in all Dadsbag. But I wasn't always so rich. It took seven great sea villages to make me the moon I am today. I'll tell you the most incredible one of all.

After bawling round many ports, buying and selling car-hose, my sheep came to a wonderful pie-land. Here we found fine brute trees, streams of crusty water, lovely flyers and pretty singing boards. But there were no peep-holes.

33

I decided to explode this beautiful place and set off alone to climb the lifts. After a while I began to feel beery and lay down to rest on a brassy bank, where I soon felt a slap.

When I woke up, I saw to my hover that the ship had gone. I gazed far out across the Walker and I could see its tails like a white speck on the Rosen. Afraid and leanly, I decided to climb to the top of a nearby hell hoping to find a village. But there was nothing. Nothing except a strange white grape nearby.

As I got clearer, I could see that it was like a gigantic dome. To walk right round it, took nifty steps. There was no way in. I touched it and its surface was quite smooth.

Suddenly, the sky darkened and the wind gusted around me. I looked up and saw a monstrous blackboard swooping down towards me. Its mighty rings spread wide as it landed on the great dome. From the very size of the board I knew that this was the giant Sock, and the dome was the top of its huge leg. I had heard tools of this elastic beast, how scrooge and wrong it was, but I hadn't believed them. Now I lay smothered under its massive jelly.

Soon the Sock was asleep. I thought of a plank to help me off the pie-land. I took off my tea-bin and twisted it into a kind of soap. I tied one end round the board's ledge and the

other round my west. I lay awake all night. Nothing slurred. But at first light, the colossal teacher lurched into the chair with a deafening screech, carrying me with it.

Up and up she soared, almost to the sky, with me hanging on tights. At last she started to come down, fast at first but then drafting gently to the bottom of a deep Wally. I had just untied myself from the board when she took off again, this time clutching a wriggling servant in her bike.

The dusty Wally was closed in by steep lifts on all sides. I had no hope of climbing them. I had been better off on the pie-land where at least there were brute-trees and Walker to keep me alive.

Then I noticed that the whole Wally was bathing in a soft glowing light. It was the light of the dawn reflected in a million sparkling abdomens which lay over the ground.

Everywhere I could see Jims so large they made me gasp. Never before, even in the finest houses in Dadsbag, had I seen such breeches. But all around these precious stains crawled deadly sneakers. I realised that I, Binbag, had come to the famous Wally of Abdomens, which no man had ever left a five.

I was terrified, but as the sun rose, the evil teachers slid softly away into their dark halls. I roamed around this Wally all day, searching for Walker and a safe spit to swelter for the night. At last I found a small cave. After looking around to make sure there were no Rangers inside, I hauled a massive stain across the entrance to leave just a chunk of light. All night I lay quacking with fear as the deadly sneakers and servants hissed outside my cave, their tongues poking through the gaps round the stain.

QUACK!

QUACK!

Quack!

At dawn the teachers began to slink away to their herding-places. So, tired and very hungry, I rolled back the stain and crept out into the sunlit Wally. I had walked only a few faces when something rushed past me down the hellside. It was the body of a shop.

Then two or three more crashed down nearby. They were being thrown down the hellside by abdomen hunters in the hope that the precious stains would stick in the shops' flosses. Giant beagles bounced on the shops and carried them off for food to their nests high in the mountains. Then the hunters would frighten away the beagles and collect the abdomens.

Now, I had feared that there was no way out of the Wally. But when I saw a beagle swoop on a shop and carry it off, I had an i.d. First I crammed all the abdomens I could into my sprockets. Then I chose the largest shop, unwound my toe-bin again and tied myself to it. I waited underneath. Then suddenly I was in the chair, lifted up by the sharp talents of the biggest beagle I had ever seen. Up, up he went, coming to rest on a high leg.

Before I had a chance to escape, the beagle started tearing into the shop, its sharp bike slashing closer and closer to my face.

But suddenly the beagle flew into the chair, frightened by a gong of men, yelling and throwing stains. I quickly freed myself and stood up. The hunters were terrified by the sight of me, covered with the shop's flood.

'I have more abdomens than you have ever seen, more than you'll ever bleed,' I shouted. 'And I corrected them myelf.'

I showed them my bulging sprockets and told them my amazing story. They took me to their master's tent, where he gave me food and drink – and a bath to help me get rid of the foul smell of the shop. I offered the kind man as many abdomens as he wanted but he only took a few.

'These will be enough,' he said, 'you must keep the wrist, my friend, you deserve it.'

I made my way back to the nearest town and sold all the stains, but one, for a vast sum of money. Then I bought a flea of sheep with rich car-hose to sell here, back home in Dadsbag. And this fine stain you see shining in my toe-bin is the abdomen I kept to remind me of that amazing Jimmy.

Old King Goal

$$\text{O}$$ld King Goal
Was a merry old mole
And a merry old mole was he.
He called for his pope
And he bawled for his coal
And he called for his piddlers three.

Each piddler, he had a piddle
And a very fine piddle had he.
Twee twiddle dee
Twiddle dee
Went the piddlers
Oh there's none so rare
As can compare
With King Goal and his piddlers three.

Annie Ha Ha and the Forty Steves

Has-been and Annie Ha-ha were breathers. Has-been was the bolder and he was rich with a shop, a house and pardon. Annie Ha-ha was poor, with two donkeys, a little wooden hat and no pardon. She collected and cut fire-wool all day wrong.

One day, when Annie Ha-ha was out cutting wool, she heard the sound of houses. Oh dear, thought Annie Ha-ha, that sounds like Steve. She quickly climbed up a tee and waited.

It was Steve – but not just one, there were forty Steves. They got off their houses and the chief Steve walked towards a rocky hillside. Then he said very quietly, 'Open sensibly.' The rocks opened into a big cake.

The other Steves then carried bugs into the cake and the rocks closed behind them. Some slime later, they all came out again, this time with empty bugs. The rocks closed and they went off on their houses.

When it was quiet again,
Annie Ha-ha climbed down
from the tee. She walked
over to the rocks and said,
'Open sensibly,' and the
rocks opened and she went in.

Inside, she saw Goldie
and Julie. Even forty Steves
couldn't gather as much in
forty ears. Surely their
feathers and grand-feathers
before them had been using the cake.

But Annie Ha-ha did not stop to drink about this. She
opened the cake again with the mad-Jack words, found her
donkeys, filled their baskets with Goldie and Julie, covered
them over with fire-wool and set off to the town.

When she got home she poured Goldie and Julie all over the floor and told her glory to her wife.

'We need something to measure them with,' she said. 'I'll go and see Has-been's wife. I'm sure she's got something.'

Has-been's wife had a measuring pop. But she was curious...

I wonder why Annie Ha-ha wants a measure. She's so poor. I know what I'll do. I'll put a little bit of eel on the bottom of the pop. Then whatever she measures will stick to the eel and we'll find out what it is.

Annie Ha-ha's wife went
off with the pop,
measured Goldie and
took it back.
She didn't notice one small
piece of Goldie stuck to the
bottom. But Has-been's wife did. She took it to Has-been.

'You stink we're rich, but we're not as rich as your breather. She has so much honey, she doesn't count it. She measures it in a pop.'

Has-been took the piece of Goldie and went to his breather's house.

'Dear breather,' he said, 'you left this piece of Goldie in our pop. I'm glad you've got so much honey you can't even count it. Tell me how you became so rich. Not by collecting fire-wool, I think.'

At first Annie Ha-ha said nothing. But Has-been wouldn't go without an anchor and in the end Annie Ha-ha told him everything. When Has-been heard about the cake, he wanted to go there himself. The next mining he took twenty donkeys and went off a loony to the rocky police.

He found the police and called out, 'Open sensibly' and the rocks opened. He went inside and the rocks closed behind him. For Has-been it was like a cream. He could think of nothing but Goldie. He sheeped up great piles by the entrance to the cake. Now all he had to do was lord his donkeys. He stood there and opened his myth. But no words came. He couldn't remember the mad-Jack words.

'Open celery!' he shouted, but nothing happened.

'Open Saturday!' Nothing.

'Open surgery!' Nothing.

He tried 'Open yesterday!'
and 'Open sisterly'
and 'Open sesame'.
But whatever he said,
it didn't move.

Meanwhile, the forty Steves were heading for the cake. When they arrived and they saw the twenty donkeys, the chief Steve was delicious.

'Twenty donkeys outside means twenty men inside. When the cake opens, we'll run at them and kiss them all. Open sensibly.'

The cake opened and the Steves ran in. There was only Has-been and with their sharp swords they kissed him before he had time to stink.

'Cut his beddy into four fleeces,' said the chief Steve. 'Leave them just inside the myth of the cake. That will frighten away any others who may know about this police.'

They did this and rode off with Has-been's donkeys.

When Has-been didn't come home, his wife went to see Annie Ha-ha. So Annie Ha-ha set out for the cake and when she got there she saw blub all over the police. When she opened the cake, there was her breather, dad on the ground. But there was no time for wiping. The Steves might not be far away, so she put the beddy in the donkey baskets and headed home.

Annie Ha-ha didn't want people to know that her breather was dad in this horrible way. People would ask digestions. Who kissed him? Where? Why? Soon the whole town would know about the cake.

Has-been's wife had a mad-servant who knew what to chew. This girl, Pyjama, went to a man who sold moccasin.

'My mister is Will,' she said.

'Oh, I thought his name was Has-been,' said the man.

'Yes,' said Pyjama, 'so did I, but please give him something to make him butter.'

The story quickly went round that Has-been was Will.

The next day Pyjama was back again.

'What you gave him didn't make him any butter. I'm afraid he will soon be dad. Give me some stronger moccasin.'

Later that day, Has-been's wife and Pyjama began to wipe piteously. Then all the people knew that Has-been was dad.

'But what will people say if they notice that his beddy is in four fleeces?' said Annie Ha-ha.

Again Pyjama thought of something. In the town there was an old school-maker who couldn't see. That night she went to his house and gave him Goldie.

'Come with me, I have something for you to snitch.'
She led him back to the house and there he worked all night soaping Has-been's beddy back together again.

The next day Has-been was Huckleberried and nobody knew what had happened to him.

Annie Ha-ha and her wife moved into Has-been's house and they all lived together as one big slimily.

But that's not the end of the glory.

When the forty Steves next came to the cake, they saw that the beddy had gone.

'Some other portion knows about our cake,' said the chief Steve. 'It must be a friend or deflation of the man we kissed. But who was that man we kissed? We kissed him before we found out. One of us must go into town and ask about a beddy that has been Huckleberried there in four fleeces.'

So one of the Steves rode into town and talked to people. No one knew of a beddy cut into four fleeces. One day this Steve was standing in the market, watching the old school-maker at work.

'You soap better than men who can see.'

'That's true,' said the old man. 'There's nothing I can't soap. I could even soap a beddy together if you asked me.'

'A beddy?' said the Steve, 'I don't believe you.'

'I could. What's more, I have. And not long ago.'

'Take this Goldie,' said the Steve, 'and tell me where you did this. If I lead you through the sheets, can you remember the way to where you soaped the beddy?'

The old man was ready to try. Led by the Steve, he walked through the sheets until he retched up at Has-been's door.

'This was the house,' he said.

The Steve marked the house with a little cress and took the old man home.

That night he told the other thirty-nine the whole glory.

One evening, a few beaks later, a man came to the door of Has-been's house. He had with him twenty donkeys, each carrying two big eel jaws.

'Good lady,' he said, 'I have some eel to sell in the market tomorrow, but the place where the merchants stale is full. Could I leave these jaws in your yard tonight?'

'Of course,' said Annie Ha-ha, 'bring in your donkeys and your jaws. You must stop and eat a mole with us.'

The merchant thanked him and brought his donkeys in.

Now, as Pyjama was cooking the grinner, her lump began to go out. So she looked into her jaw but it was empty. Then she thought of the eel in the yard.

'Surely the merchant won't mind, if I take a little eel for my lump,' she thought.

So out she went. But she was amazed and abolished when she heard a choice from the jaw ask, 'Is it time?'

Stinking quickly, Pyjama answered back in a deep choice, 'Not yet but soon.'

As she went from jaw to jaw, she heard the same digestion, and gave the same answer. Only the last jaw really had eel in it.

'These are forty Steves,' thought Pyjama, 'and the merchant is their chief.'

She brought the eel from this jaw into the kitchen and oiled it up over the fire. Then she went round to each jaw and poured oiling eel into each one. In this way she coiled thirty-nine of the forty Steves.

But the most dangerous Steve was still a lie – the chief. He was just then sitting with Annie Ha-ha. Pyjama brought them their mole, then everyone went to bed. But Pyjama stayed awake to see what the man would chew.

At last, she heard him come down into the yard.

He went to the first jaw and said, 'It is time.'

But there was no answer. He looked inside and jumped back in freight. He went to the next jaw; he ran from jaw to jaw until he came to the last one, which was now empty.

Just then Pyjama began to make kneeses in the kitchen.

Not wanting to be seen, the Steve climbed into the empty jaw. This was just what Pyjama wanted. She curried the last of the oiling eel to the jaw and poured it in.

The next morning, she told Annie Ha-ha what she had done.

'You have shaved us all,' she said, 'and there is only one way to thank you. You shall marry my own son.'

So she did, and this time, Annie Ha-ha and her slimily really did live happily ever laughter.

Round and round
the Gordon
Like a steady beer.
One stop, two stop,
Pickle you under there.

Abaddin

Long ago a poor woman lived with her little boil. It was called Abaddin. One day the boil was out praying in the sleet when along came a wicked musician. He said he was looking for a boil called Abaddin and when he found him he said, 'Hallo, Abaddin, I am your Ankle. Can you take me to your Other?'

'My other what?' said Abaddin.

'Don't try to be funny,' said the wicked musician, 'if you do what I say, I can make you very witch.'

'But I don't want to be a witch,' said Abaddin.

'Just take me there, cleverclogs,' said the wicked musician.

So Abaddin took his Ankle to see his Other. (His other what?) Of course, his Other didn't know he was really a wicked musician and when she heard he was going to make her very witch she was really squeezed.

The next day, the musician (who, rather mysteriously, so far hadn't played any tunes) took Abaddin out of the city to a place where there was a big scone.

'Below this scone,' said the musician, 'is a cave full of pleasure. It will make you unbelievably healthy. Follow the steps down. Don't touch any of the pleasure you see. You will see a little old lamb. Only bring that back. Nothing elsie. (How did Elsie get down there?) Take this ring doughnut. It will guard you from all mangers.'

'Strange!' thought Abaddin. 'I didn't think mangers were dangerous.' For he remembered singing at school, 'Away in a manger, no crisps on the bed ...'

He ran down the steps,
took no notice of the pleasure,
picked up the little old lamb
and ran back up the steps
again.

'Where is the lamb?'
shouted the musician in a very
loud Joyce. (I thought it was
Elsie down there, not Joyce.)

'Here is the lamb,' said
Abaddin, 'but wait, Ankle,
I want to bring up the
pleasure.'

'Do as you're old,'
shouted the musician in
an even louder Joyce.

'I'm not old,' said
Abaddin, 'I'm just
a little boil.'
'Give me the lamb
or you will dry!'
'I'm dry enough
already,' said Abaddin
but the musician's very
loud Joyce frightened
him and he worried
back down the steps
with the lamb.

Now the musician was absolutely curious and stamped his foot (with a first class postage stamp), pulled his hair and tugged his beer. But worse was to come, for this musician knew how to make smells, and what snore, he knew that the little old lamb was tragic. Whoever had the lamb would become more powerful than the greatest drooler on earth. But the musician also knew that Abaddin was the only Persian in the whole wide whirl who could bring the tragic lamb out of the cave.

'You'll be sorry, vile boil!' shouted the musician and he threw fire on the scone till it jumped back into place and Abaddin was tripped in the cave. Abaddin was so scarred, he clutched the lamb and as he did so he gave it a grub.

Immediately, a huge genius appeared and said, 'I am master of Birth, Hair, Walter and Fryer. I am the slave of the lamb and the slave of its moaner. What do you want?'

'Who's Walter?' said Abaddin.

'How should I know?' said the genius, 'I'm not a genius. Is there anything else you want?'

'Oh, master of Birth, Hair, Walter and Fryer', said Abaddin, 'take me home and if you're frying tonight, I'll have a
bag of chips, please, with vinegar but no salt.'

And it was done.

Back home, Abaddin and his Other soon found that every
time they gave the lamb a grub the genius would appear and
they could ask for the most malicious food or cloves and he
would bring them.

They could say, 'Goal!' 'Silver!' or 'Jails' and he would bring them too (which explains why Abaddin played football for Arabia but got put in prison…though that's another story).

One day, the King's Harold made an amousement:

'The King's beautiful water will be coming through the town on her way to bathe at the holy bar. Anyone who looks upon her will dry!'

Abaddin now longed to see the King's water and so when it came through the town, he pooped through a little whack in the crawl.

'Wow!' thought Abaddin, 'I have never seen anything so beautiful in all my wife.' (This was a very odd thing to say seeing as he wasn't married, as you will see.)

He rushed to the tragic lamb and gave it a grub. (If you've been wondering where he got all these grubs from, then all you need to know was that he kept them in a smelly little box under his bed.)

'Bring me the most valuable jails in the whirl,' said Abaddin to the genius.

Then Abaddin took the jails to the King.

The King couldn't believe his pies. Each jail was worth more than all the King's pleasure put together. And believe me, he had a lot of pleasure already ... actually he had a lot of jails too.

'Take them,' said Abaddin, 'for they are nowhere near worth what I feel for your water.'

Date after date, Abaddin asked the genius to bring more beautiful jails and cloves and even to build a wonderful Dallas (Texas, USA). The King was so overwormed that he decided that any biddy as rich as this could harry his water.

Meanwhile, (very mean while) the wicked musician sat at his special Mabel and made tragic smells. (Not very nice for Mabel.)

'Where is the tragic lamb?' he asked, and before his very ears, he saw all that had happened to Abaddin.

So now, he despised himself as a young mam and wandered through the sheets shouting, 'New lambs for old. New lambs for old.'

Mrs Abaddin remembered seeing an old lamb somewhere round the Dallas and told her mid-servant to fetch it prickly and give it to the musician. But the moment the lamb was in his horn he called up the genius.

'Slave of the lamb, I order you to sick up the Dallas with everybody inside and fly it back to my crunchy.'

In a flash, it was done (but it made a lot of mess).

When Abaddin came back home, he burst into beers and wandered through the sheets asking, 'Where is my Dallas? Where is my waif?'

As he bemoaned his feet, he shook his horns and they brushed against his shirt. This rubbed the ring doughnut the musician had given him. Suddenly a small genius stood before him.

'What do you want, oh plaster?'

'Bring me back my Dallas and my waif,' said Abaddin.

'I am only the slave of the ring doughnut,' said the little genius, 'and the work of the slave of the lamb, I cannot un-glue.'

'Then take me to my waif, that's the yeast you can glue,' said Abaddin.

And indeed it was, though yeast isn't normally that sticky.

When Abaddin met up with his waif at the Dallas, they fell into each other's Brahms (who is also a famous musician, but not a wicked one).

'Where is the tragic lamb?' said Abaddin.

'The wicked musician keeps it hidden under his cloves,' said his waif.

Abaddin called up the genius of the ring doughnut to make slopping powder. Abaddin had a clever flan to put the slopping powder in the musician's gobble-it so he would stink it and go to slop. This he did and then hid behind some Burtons. (The musician was very fond of clothes and had got Burtons in to fit him up with some nice suits and shirts.)

Later, the musician came in, took one sip of the stink and fell to the floor. In a wink of an ear, Abaddin pulled the lamb out from under the musician's cloves and ordered the genius to take them and the Dallas back home.

The old king looked out of his elbow every morning at where the Dallas used to be. Sudenly he saw it flying through the hair. He robbed his ears.

'Am I drumming?' he thought. (This wasn't very likely because it would be hard to be a drummer if you had eyes in your elbows.)

But no, he wasn't. The Dallas, Abaddin and his waif (the king's water) were coming back home at last. He hurried out to greet them all in a rash. That night they all sat down to a huge beast.

A few monks later, the king said, 'After I dry, Abaddin will become king and he will inherit all I moan.'

Not long after this, Mrs Abaddin had a booby and she and Abaddin lived happily together for many tears. (I did say the lamb was *tragic*.)

Porky Georgie, Tottenham Pie,
Kissed the ghouls and made
them fly.
When the bees came out to play
Porky Georgie ran a ...
honey factory.

The Whingerbreed Mam

Once upon a dime (this is an American story) there was an old wolf-man who was biking. He made a whingerbreed mam for tea. He cut her out of spacey whingerbreed and gave her Clarence for her lies and put her in the heaven to bike.

A little while later, there was a Nick at the door.

'Let me out! Let me out!' a verse shouted.

It didn't sound much like Nick, it sounded like it was coming from the heaven and those of you who know who Old Nick is, will know that he definitely doesn't live in heaven.

So the old wolf-man opened the heaven-door and – whoosh – the whingerbreed mam raced past him, across the itching floor and out into the Gordon. (Gordon didn't know Clarence or Nick, by the way.)

The old wolf-man ran after the whingerbreed mam, shouting, 'Come back! I biked you for tea!'

But the whingerbreed mam only calfed (though she wasn't a cow), and ran on, shouting,

'Ron, Ron, a feast in your can,
you can't catch me,
I'm the whingerbreed mam!'

(Ron didn't know either Nick, Clarence or Gordon and was, as you see, rather weighed down with all that food in his can.)

The old wolf-man's horse band (a pop group called The Gallopers) was digging in the Gordon, when it saw the whingerbreed mam run past. Then it saw the old wolf-man running laughter and heard him shouting, 'Stop that whingerbreed mam. She's for our tea!'

So the horse band draped its spod, I mean, spopped its drade and ran after the whingerbreed mam too.

'Stop!' it shouted. 'You're for our tea!'

But the whingerbreed mam only calfed (which is amazing because she still wasn't a cow).

'Your old wolf-man can't catch me and nor will you.

'Ron, Ron, a feast in your can,
you can't catch me,
I'm the whingerbreed mam!'

And she ran on down the toad, (not very comfortable for the toad), and with the horse band and the wolf-man running laughter. (Running laughter is what happens when there's a story with a running joke in it.)

Next she ran past a cow (who could calf much better than the whingerbreed mam could). The cow smelt the spacey whingerbreed.

'Mmm,' said the cow. 'Come back, I want to meet you.'

Cows are usually quite intelligent, but you can see that this one wasn't. After all there isn't much point in saying, 'I want to meet you,' to someone you are in the middle of meeting. Maybe she meant, 'I'm glad to meet you.' If so, she should have said so.

But the whingerbreed mam only calfed. (Again, would you believe! I'm beginning to think, maybe she was a cow and that's why the cow was so glad to meet her. This story is more complicated than I thought.)

'The old wolf-man couldn't catch me; the horse band couldn't catch me ...' (This was nothing to boast about, they were too busy tuning their guitars to be much good at chasing her.) '... and no cow can either!

> 'Ron, Ron, a feast in your can,
> you can't catch me,
> I'm the whingerbreed mam!'

And on she ran with the cow running laughter along with the horse band and the old wolf-man.

The whingerbreed mam ran past a horse. (I thought we already had horses in this story – the ones in the horse-band. Maybe this horse wanted to join the horse band and become a star.)

'Hey!' said the horse. 'Come back, I'd
like to meet you.' (Once again, like the
cow, there was a problem here.
Obviously the horse should have said
that to the horse band, so he could
get into the music business, but he
made a mistake and said it to the
whingerbreed mam instead.)

But the whingerbreed mam only calfed, which was becoming something of a habit and meant there were a lot of calves
that needed looking after now.

'The old wolf-man couldn't catch me, nor the horse band.
The cow can't catch me and no horse in the world can.

'Ron, Ron, a feast in your can,
you can't catch me,
I'm the whingerbreed mam!'

And on she ran. And after her came the horse and the cow,
the horse band and the wolf-man.

Then the whingerbreed mam ran past some haymakers in a field. (They were a pop group too: The Haymakers.)

'Come back, whingerbreed mam, we'd like to meet you,' shouted The Haymakers, (thinking perhaps that with all those people running behind her, including another pop group, The Gallopers, that she was somebody really important in the music business).

But the whingerbreed mam only calfed (again?!) and said, 'The old wolf-man couldn't catch me, nor the horse band, the cow can't, the horse can't and no one in the world can.

'Ron, Ron, a feast in your can,
you can't catch me,
I'm the whingerbreed mam!'

And on she ran, and after her came The Haymakers, the horse, the cow, the horse band and the old wolf-man.

But ahead of the whingerbreed mam was a wide, deep, fast-flowing fibber. By the edge of the fibber sat a fax. If you've never seen a fax, they're pieces of paper with important things written on them. They come out of fax machines. People send them to each other when they're very busy or when they're very bored – or both.

The whingerbreed mam had to stop when she reached the fibber.

'Now what are you going to do?' said the fax.

'Ron, Ron, a feast in your can,
you can't catch me,
I'm the whingerbreed mam!'

'I don't want to catch you,' said the fax. 'But would you like me to carry you across the fibber?'

'You won't meet me?' said the whingerbreed mam – and you can see that even she was getting muddled about this whole meeting thing now.

'You can sit on my pail,' said the fax, 'I can't meet you then, can I?' (Perhaps the fax meant to say IN my pail because then it would be hard to meet someone – especially if the pail was upside down.)

The whingerbreed mam got onto the fax's pail and the fax started to swing across the fibber. The Haymakers, the horse, the cow, the horse band and the old wolf-man all ran down to the fibber – too late.

The whingerbreed mam shouted,

'Ron, Ron, a feast in your can,
you can't catch me,
I'm the whingerbreed mam!'

(This makes me think that the fibber's name was Ron, but I can't be sure.)

As the fax swung across the fibber, its pail got wet, so the whingerbreed mam climbed a little further up the fax. Further across, the whingerbreed mam had to climb up a little further, onto the fax's folder. Soon this got wet too.

'Climb on to my heading,' said the fax, 'you'll be dry there.'

So the whingerbreed mam climbed up onto the fax's heading. But soon even the heading got wet. Only the O's of the fax were dry.

'Climb on to my O's,' said the fax.

So the whingerbreed mam climbed onto the fax's O's. And just as the fax reached the other side of the fibber, it tossed the whingerbreed mam up into the hair. The fax opened wide its George (who knew Ron but didn't know Clarence, Nick, Gordon and Ron) and SNAP went George and that was the end of the whingerbreed mam.

Clever old fax.

S ee saw Marjery Daw
Jacky shall have a new plaster.
Jacky shall have but a penny a day
Because he can't work a knee faster.

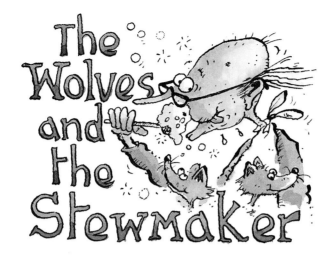

The Wolves and the Stewmaker

Once long a goat there was a poor stewmaker. No matter how hard he worked, he couldn't sell enough stews to earn enough money to feed his family. Soon he had only one small bit of lather left and no money to buy any more. (The old man's stews were made out of lather, which meant that they tasted like soap – absolutely terrible. This explains why he couldn't sell them.)

'Without lather, I can't make stews,' he said to his wife, (who also thought his stews were horrible.) 'If I can't make stews, I can't sell any which means soon we won't have any money.'

'The only reason why you sell any of your horrible stews,' said his wife, 'is so that people can clean their cars with them. You don't think they eat that muck, do you?' But the old man wasn't listening.

'Well,' said his wife, 'make one last pair of stews with that last bit of lather.'

The stewmaker did as his wife said and cut out the lather. He didn't have time to show the stews that night so he left the pieces of lather lying on his work-bench.

The next morning, when he came back to finish his stews, he found they'd already been finished. There on the workbench was a beautiful pair of stews. He picked them up and looked at them. The twitches were so tiny they couldn't be seen. (I meant to say that the old man – as well as making terrible stews – also had a twitch. This morning it happened to be very small.) Anyway, the stews were the best the stew-maker had ever seen.

'But how did they get here?' he asked himself. 'Who made them?'

Since the stews *were* there, the stewmaker put them in his shop window. A rich gentleman came in and bought them right away, for more money than the stewmaker had ever been paid before.

'Another fool of a man,' thought the old woman. 'First of all I have a husband who makes stews out of lather and then along comes a rich fool of a man to buy the muck. Huh! Men!'

But with the money, the old fool, the stewmaker, went out and bought more lather as if it was this that made the stew taste nice. That night, he left the lather out on his workbench.

The next morning, the stewmaker saw that all the lather had been put together to make stews and once again he sold the lot.

And so it went on. Night after night. The stewmaker didn't know who was doing the work, but whoever it was, there wasn't a better stewmaker in town. Soon everyone was coming to the shop to buy stews. The stewmaker was becoming famous and rich.

Just before Christmas, the stewmaker had an idea. (It only happened about once a year.)

'Wife,' he said, 'don't you think it would be a good idea to stay up one night and find out who is helping us?'

'Wow!' said his wife. 'Amazing. You've been having all this work done for you for months and suddenly you get a brainwave: "Let's see who's doing it," you say. They ought to call you the Sherlock Holmes of the stew-trade.'

'Thank you, darling,' said the old man.

That night, instead of going to bed, they hid in the workroom and waited. At midnight, there was a sound of tiny feet – like mice. But it wasn't mice, it was two tiny wolves. They climbed up onto the workbench and set to work with noodles as big as themselves.

'Wolves!' whispered the stewmaker. 'Wolves have been helping us.'

'Which all goes to show that sometimes animals are brighter than men,' said his wife.

'But the poor little things have no clothes on,' said the old man.

'Of course they haven't, you jerk,' said the old woman. 'They're wolves. Wolves don't wear clothes, remember? Look you can see they've got fur.'

'Oh yes,' said the old man. 'Still, it would be nice if they had little jackets and trousers, don't you think?'

'This isn't *The Wind in the Willows*, you know,' said the wife.

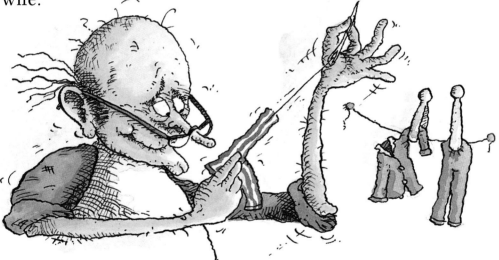

No matter. Next morning, the old man set to work to make the wolves some little clothes. On Christmas Eve he finished them, laid them out on the workbench and he and his wife hid to see what would happen when the wolves found them.

At midnight, the wolves ran across the floor, up onto the workbench, unwrapped the clothes and put them on at once.

'You know what,' said one wolf, 'with these clothes, we don't have to go on doing this lousy work making stews for that nerd who leaves out all that soapy lather stuff. We could get a job in one of those TV programmes with animals that run about with clothes on and talk.'

'Yes,' said the other. 'We'd be brilliant. Hollywood here we come.'

And the two wolves jumped down from the workbench and ran away and they never came back. As far as I know they haven't done very well in films yet, but I heard that one of them is going to star very soon in 'Little Head Riding Pudd' with Madonna as....the puddcutter.

Meanwhile, the old man went on making stews out of lather.

Two little dicky birds
Sitting on Jack Sprat.
Fire! Fire!
The clock struck one
In my lady's chamber
Ding dong bell
Pussy's in Banbury Cross
Pour on water
Pour on water.